Make all the units match b

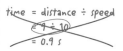

Maths questions often have a mixture of units, to check ıı ууu..
So — you need to be careful with all your calculations.

1) Don't jump straight in with your size tens.

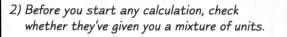

2) Before you start any calculation, check whether they've given you a mixture of units.

3) If there's a mixture of, say, cm and m, do the conversions first.

(It's generally easier to convert into the units that won't involve loads of decimals. Up to you.)

Beware of conversions with time — especially if decimals are involved.

4) Then do the calculation.

A toy car travels 9 m at 10 cm/s.
How long does it take?

$\text{time} = \text{distance} \div \text{speed}$
~~$= 9 \div 10$~~
~~$= 0.9 \text{ s}$~~

WRONG — you need them
ALL in m or ALL in cm.

$9 \text{ m} = 900 \text{ cm}$

RIGHT — convert m to cm
and it'll all work beautifully.

$\text{time} = \text{distance} \div \text{speed}$

$= 900 \div 10$

$= 90 \text{ s}$

Include units in the answer

And make sure they're sensible — read the
question back to yourself, along with your answer.
E.g. if you find yourself saying: "How long does it
take? 9 metres..." then it's clearly the wrong unit.

It could be 90 of anything if you don't put a unit afterwards...

90 seconds?

90 years?

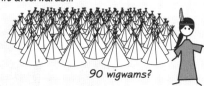

90 wigwams?

Mark it wrong if you forget the units

Even when you're practising, don't give yourself any marks for a question unless
you've remembered the units and got them right.
You've just <u>got to</u> get into the habit of including units.

Tip 2:

Make Sure Your Answer isn't Ridiculous

It seems blummin' obvious, but if you just say "That's obvious, so I won't bother with it," you WILL slip up. What you need to do is make really sure you check, after every question, that your answer is not too big, too small or too weird.

Tip 2 — Make Sure Your Answer isn't Ridiculous

Your answers should make sense

1) Don't go thinking maths doesn't make sense. However bewildering what you learn may be, your answers have got to be sensible.

2) Just check that:

They're not ridiculously big.

They're not ridiculously small.

After every question, check it's realistic

1) You don't have to know exact heights, weights or whatever.

Examples:

Calculate Bill's height.

5 metres? — nope (unless Bill's a monster).
2.24 cm? — nope (unless Bill's a slug).
224 cm? — sounds a bit big, so best check your answer to be sure.
1.63 metres — sounds reasonable.

2) Make sure it's vaguely reasonable. Normally if you make a mistake, it'll be a big one.

How long till the next bus?

1 minute 20 seconds — it's just possible, but sounds unlikely. Best check your answer to be sure.
0.03 seconds — no way.
4 hours — possible, if you live in the middle of nowhere, but check.
12 minutes — feasible.

Bearings

450° — nope, it's got to be between 0° and 360°.
172° — could be.

Tip 3:

Get Your
Scatter Graphs
Right

Scatter graphs are <u>always</u> popping up in exams — and they're <u>easy marks</u>.
Make sure you don't miss out — use this method <u>every time</u> you practise a
question — then it'll be second nature by the time you get in the exam.

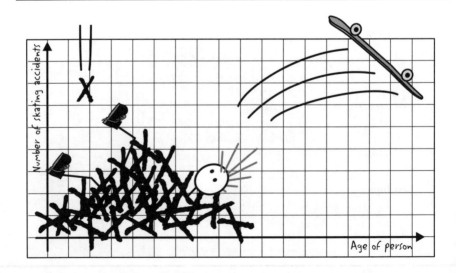

Tip 3 — Get Your Scatter Graphs Right

Follow this method <u>every time</u> you do a practice question...

Make your graph look nice

You might not think that neatness is that important, but with graphs it definitely is.

1) Always use a pencil. Then you can rub out your mistakes.

2) Give the graph a title.

3) Label the axes and include the units.

Plot the points carefully

4) Plot the points by drawing crosses — they're much easier to read than splodges.

5) Do it accurately. The point should be marked by the <u>centre</u> of the cross.

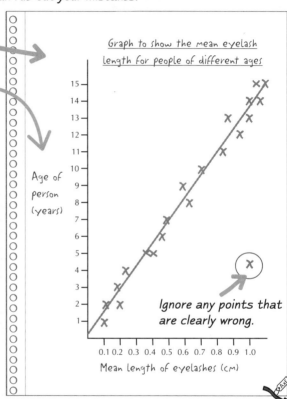

Graph to show the mean eyelash length for people of different ages

Age of person (years)

Ignore any points that are clearly wrong.

Mean length of eyelashes (cm)

The line of best fit should have the same number of points either side

5) How to draw the line of best fit:
- use a ruler
- the line should <u>follow the trend</u> of the points
- you should have the <u>same number of points either side</u> of the line

Don't worry how many points are on the line itself. The line of best fit is only representing the <u>trend</u>.

Tip 4:

Beware of Brackets

Brackets aren't complicated — in theory. But in that exam it's a whole different ball game, and that's exactly when you start doing daft things. So, rule of thumb: whenever you see brackets, alarm bells should start ringing.

Tip 4 — Beware of Brackets

Multiply <u>everything</u> inside the bracket

If there's a multiplier before a bracket, it applies to <u>everything</u> inside the bracket. Always <u>double-check</u> your work to see that you haven't missed any terms out.

e.g. $3(2a + 4) = 3{\times}2a + (3{\times}4) = 6a + 12$

<u>don't forget this bit</u>

Use FOIL to multiply out two brackets

If there are two brackets, <u>everything</u> inside the first bracket needs to be multiplied by <u>everything</u> inside the second. Always use FOIL — and <u>double-check</u> it afterwards.

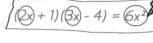

First $(2x + 1)(3x - 4) = 6x^2$ Multiply the first bits and write the result down.

Outside $(2x + 1)(3x - 4) = 6x^2 + (-8x)$ Then do the outside bits...

Inside $(2x + 1)(3x - 4) = 6x^2 + (-8x) + 3x$ ...then the insides...

Last $(2x + 1)(3x - 4) = 6x^2 + (-8x) + 3x + (-4)$ ...then the last bit of each bracket. Then just add it all up.

$$= 6x^2 - 5x - 4$$

Remember — a bracket squared is two brackets multiplied together — so it's FOIL again: $(2x + 1)^2 = (2x + 1)(2x + 1)$

Loads of people make these mistakes
— make sure YOU DON'T

1 $3(a + b) = 3a + b$ ✗

Should be $3a + 3b$ ✓

2 $(3a)^2 = 3a^2$ ✗

Should be $9a^2$ ✓

3 $(x + 2)^2 = x^2 + 4$ ✗

Should be $(x + 2)(x + 2)$
$= x^2 + 4x + 4$ ✓

Tip 5:

Get to Know Your Calculator

OK, I know, I know — OF COURSE you know how to use a calculator. But there's a world of difference between doing simple additions on a calculator and confidently working out fractions, using the powers button and storing answers in the memory (and retrieving them again).

Sort out the basics first

1) Make sure you know how to use those buttons for calculations on your calculator.

2) For the ones you don't know, work out how to use them (find out from your teacher, your revision guide or whatever).

3) Write out how to do each one like this:

Brackets:

Work out $\dfrac{3 \times (7 + 9)}{4 - (8 - 6)}$:

Answer should be 24.

4) Practise loads and loads of calculations so you can do them with your eyes closed in the exam.

Remember to still write out your working (see Tip 11).

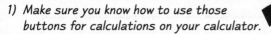

You should have **no problem** <u>at all</u> with using all the following buttons:

(goes without saying)

If you can't use brackets you'll make a lot of work for yourself.

 (and $\sin^{-1}$ etc.) or kiss those trig questions goodbye

Basically, just learn whatever powers buttons your calc has.

Fancier buttons make life easier...

These are the buttons that will save you loads of time in the exam.

If you've got time — figure out how to use them, write out the methods and learn them.

 The fraction button.

 or The standard form button. Saves you typing × 10 x^y 5.

 The $\dfrac{1}{x}$ button.

 For converting time to hours, minutes and seconds

STO The 'add to memory' button. Use it to store bits of or Min calculations until you need them...

RCL ...then use the 'recall' button to or MR bring them up again.

...but only use the ones you're sure about

1) If you're not totally sure how a button works — DON'T USE IT.

2) The exam is not the right place to figure it out.

3) If you haven't learnt it before you go in there, do it the long way and write out all your working (see Tip 11).

4) It's much safer to use methods you're used to. You <u>know</u> they work.

Tip 6:

Use Formula Triangles

You've gotta learn the <u>formulas</u> for solving maths problems, or you'll throw away <u>easy marks</u>. Formula triangles make it <u>easy</u> to learn formulas — you only need to <u>learn 1 formula</u>, and put it in a triangle to learn <u>2 more</u> with no extra effort.

Tip 6 — Use Formula Triangles

Decide where the letters go...

1) If 2 letters are multiplied together in the formula, they go on the bottom of the triangle (so the other one goes on top).

E.g. d = s × t fits into the triangle like this:

2) If one thing's divided by another in the formula, then the one on top of the division goes on top in the triangle (it doesn't matter which way round the other two go on the bottom).

E.g. — sin = opp/hyp fits into the triangle like this:

Use your thumb...

1) Using formula triangles is dead easy. Put your thumb over the thing you want to find, then write down what's left showing — this gives you your calculation.

2) Then put in the values for the other two things and work it out.

Get your units right...

The UNITS you get out of the formula depend entirely on the UNITS you put into it.

Example: 'Using "d = s × t", find the value of "s" when d = 20 m and t = 50 s.

Answer: You want to find "s", so cover "s" up. That leaves d/t showing (i.e. d÷t). So s = d/t. If you put in the numbers you get s = 20÷50 = 0.4

E.g. If you put distance in cm and time in seconds into the triangle, then the speed must come out in cm per second.

0.4 cm/s

Tip 7:
Know Your Algebra Jargon

There are only a handful of <u>different types</u> of algebra questions.
If you know exactly what they all <u>mean</u> then you won't have to spend
vital exam time figuring out what you're actually being asked to <u>do</u>.

$a =$ 🙂
$b =$ 📕

Practise the five main types of question

These types of algebra question crop up again and again. Learn the key words and *practise doing them* — so you don't waste time in the exam.

1) __Solve:__
Pretty obvious — you have to work out what number x, y, etc. stands for.

Solve this equation:
$3x + 21 = 30$ **(2 marks)**

$3x = 30 - 21 = 9$
$x = 3$

2) __Expand:__
Multiply out the brackets.

Expand:
$3x^2(2x^2 + 3x - 4)$ **(2 marks)**

$(3x^2 \times 2x^2) + (3x^2 \times 3x) + (3x^2 \times (-4))$
$= 6x^4 + 9x^3 - 12x^2$

3) __Simplify:__
This means things like collecting like terms, multiplying out brackets and cancelling common factors in fractions.

Simplify the following expressions:
(a) $3x(2x + 3) - 5x^2$ **(2 marks)**

multiplying out brackets: $6x^2 + 9x - 5x^2$
collecting x^2 terms: $x^2 + 9x$

(b) $\dfrac{3x^3}{12x^2}$ **(2 marks)**

Cancel $3x^2$ from top and bottom: $\dfrac{x}{4}$

4) __Factorise:__
Put brackets in and pull out any common factors.

Factorise the following expression:
$2x^2 + 7x$ **(1 mark)**

only factor is x: $x(2x + 7)$

5) __Rearrange:__
This is just manipulating a formula like x = blah blah to make it y = blah blah.

Rearrange this formula to make v the subject:
$E = \frac{1}{2}mv^2$ **(2 marks)**

Get rid of fraction: $2E = mv^2$
Put m on other side: $\dfrac{2E}{m} = v^2$
Take square root: $v = \sqrt{\dfrac{2E}{m}}$

Tip 8:

Find the Easy Angles First

You know that kind of question where they only give you one angle and you have to find another... but they're nowhere near each other and you haven't got a clue where to start... Best way to tackle them is: START WITH THE EASY ANGLES.

Tip 8 — Find the Easy Angles First

Learn the angle rules

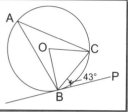

For angles questions like these, you need to know the angle rules.
If you don't, you'll be absolutely STUFFED on the day.
Get out your revision guide and learn them all now.
(They'll be under the heading "Geometry" and will go along the lines of "angles in a triangle add up to 180" and stuff.)

In the CGP books the angle rules are on: p20-23 in the higher book,
p36-39 in the intermediate book and p11-13 in the foundation book

Always start with the easy angles

When you get an angles question like this, the first rule is: Don't Panic.

A, B and C are points on a circle.
O is the centre of the circle.
P lies on a tangent to the circle at B.

Find angle BAC.

1) **Work out all the angles that are obvious** from the angle they've given you. **Don't worry about which angle they're asking you to find.**

2) Look at the angles you've just put in — see what other angles have become obvious.

3) **Now** look at the angle they're asking for. If you haven't already found it, it'll be much easier now.

Remember to look for:
angles in a triangle,
angles in a quadrilateral,
parallel lines, symmetry, etc.
intersecting lines,
circles, tangents, etc.

Example:

1) Start with the *obvious* angles.
   Here you use the TANGENT-RADIUS rule.

2) Look at the angle you've just put in.
   The ISOSCELES FROM TWO RADII rule gives you a second angle,
   then you can use the ANGLES IN A TRIANGLE rule to get the other.

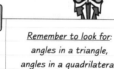

3) *Now* look at the angle they're asking for.
   The ANGLE AT THE CENTRE IS TWICE THAT AT THE CIRCUMFERENCE
   rule gives you the one you're after.

Tip 9:

Simultaneous Equations Crash Course

You'll get a simultaneous equations question in the exam, sure as eggs are eggs. So what you gonna do. You're gonna read this tip, discover that they're not that bad after all, and get all the marks for the question in the exam. That's what.

$$2x + 3y = 31$$
$$x - 3y = 2$$

All simultaneous equation questions are like this:

This method should be in your revision guide too — if you haven't learnt if yet then DO IT NOW.

> Solve this pair of simultaneous equations:
> 3x + y = 10
> 2y − x = 6   *(3 marks)*

1) Rearrange to get x and y bits in the same order — then number both equations.

$3x + y = 10$ — 1

Rearrange second equation:

$-x + 2y = 6$ — 2

Double equation 1:

$6x + 2y = 20$ — 3

2) Multiply one equation by a convenient multiplier, then renumber.

You're trying to get the same number of 'x's or 'y's in each equation.

3) Add or subtract equations to get rid of y.

Subtract equation 2 from equation 3, term by term:

$6x - (-x) + 2y - 2y = 20 - 6$

$7x = 14$

$x = 2$

4) Solve for x.

5) Substitute x into one of the original equations...

Substitute x = 2 back into equation 1:

$(3 \times 2) + y = 10$

$6 + y = 10$

$y = 10 - 6$

$y = 4$

...and use it to find y.

Check it works — substitute x = 2 and y = 4 into equation 2:

$-2 + (2 \times 4) = 6$

6) Check it.

Learn that method and you'll be fine

Practise it till your pen bleeds.

Tip 10:

Use Clever
Memory Tricks

When you've got a whopping great <u>list</u> of things to learn in a certain order, make up a <u>word</u> or <u>phrase</u> from the first letters. It'll help you remember the list and it means you can store 10,000 times as much info in your brain (NB: rough guess).

Use the memory tricks you've already learned

1) Use memory tricks when you have to remember any list of things.

2) There are a few that you've probably seen before. They come in two categories:

Words made from first letters ('acronyms')

e.g. Sohcahtoa

Sentences made from first letters ('mnemonics')

e.g. Seven Old Hags Cook Anchovies, Haddock, Trout Or Angelfish.

(I find Sohcahtoa easier to remember.)

Sin = Opposite **over** Hypotenuse,
Cos = Adjacent **over** Hypotenuse,
Tan = Opposite **over** Adjacent.
— both tricks help you remember the trigonometry rules.

Make up your own tricks

1) Start with a paragraph of your notes. →

2) Reduce the paragraph down to a few key words.

3) Then write out the first letters of each word in the list.

4) If there are a few vowels and it doesn't matter about the order of the list, try and rearrange the letters into a word.

(That doesn't apply here because the letters need to stay in order.)

5) If there are no vowels or if the order is important, make a sentence using the first letters.

6) Try and include one of your friends' names, and make it funny or rude.

(It doesn't have to be funny.)

When you're transforming graphs, for (x – a) you shift the plotted line right, and for (y – a) you shift the line up. (It's the opposite of what you expect.)

Transforming graphs:
X minus a Right
Y minus a Up

Transforming graphs:
XMAR
YMAU

Transforming graphs:
X Marks Andrew's Rear
Your Mates Are Ugly

Tip 11:

Show ALL Your Working

In the exam always write down EACH STAGE of your working — JUST IN CASE.
Here's why — 1. You can LOSE MARKS if you DON'T show your working.
2. If you mess up somewhere, you can still GET MARKS if the METHOD'S RIGHT.
3. It's much EASIER TO CHECK your answer at the end.

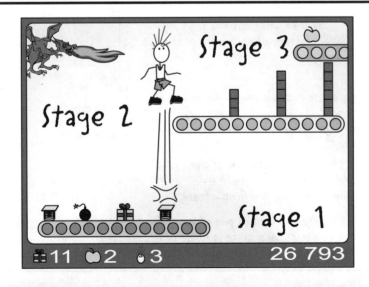

Tip 11 — Show ALL Your Working

Write down every step

A cylinder holds 1500 cm³ of water. It is 15 cm high.
Find the radius of the cylinder.

(4 marks)

1) *Quote the formula (if you're using one).*

$$\text{volume of cylinder, } V = \pi r^2 h$$

2) *Make it clear when you're substituting in.*

substituting in: $1500 = 3.14 \times r^2 \times 15$

3) *Write the expression out before and after rearranging it.*

$$1500 = 47.1 \times r^2$$
$$1500 \div 47.1 = r^2$$
$$31.847 = r^2$$

(Write down the equation every time you rearrange it.)

take square root: $r = 5.6$ cm

Write algebra answers on separate lines

Showing clear working is CRUCIAL in algebra.

Solve the equation $3(x + 4) = 2x - 5$

(2 marks)

1) *Write each step on a separate line.*

Multiply out brackets: $3x + 12 = 2x - 5$

2) *Explain each step — even if it's obvious. Then the examiner can see what you're doing — even if you get it wrong.*

Gather the x terms on left: $3x + 12 - 2x = -5$

Gather numbers on right: $3x - 2x = -5 - 12$

Simplify: $x = -17$

it's handy to line up the = signs

"And now I am going to pull the rabbit from the hat."

Even do it with simple calculations

Even with the simplest calculations you can press the wrong button.

A pair of shorts worth £19.50 is reduced in the sale by 30%.
What is the new price of the shorts?

(3 marks)

Get into the habit of writing down the calculation you're going to do.

Reduction = 30% of £19.50 = £19.50 × 0.3 = £5.85

Selling Price = £19.50 - £5.85 = £25.35

Do it with every practice question you do.

*D'oh — I hit plus instead of minus, so this answer's wrong.
But I still get 2 marks because my method was right.*

Why not collect the lot?

Ask not what you can do for CGP, ask what CGP can do for you.

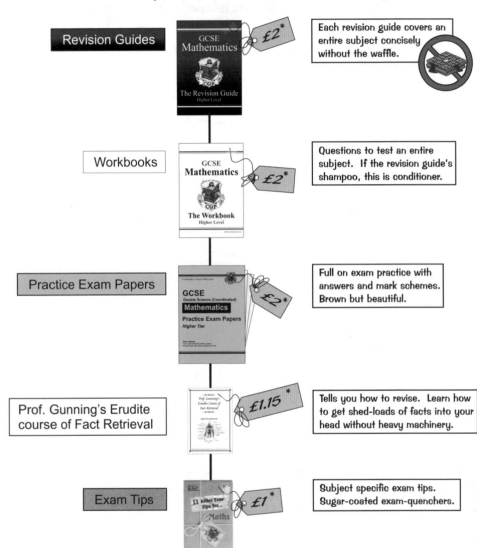

| Revision Guides | £2* | Each revision guide covers an entire subject concisely without the waffle. |

| Workbooks | £2* | Questions to test an entire subject. If the revision guide's shampoo, this is conditioner. |

| Practice Exam Papers | £2* | Full on exam practice with answers and mark schemes. Brown but beautiful. |

| Prof. Gunning's Erudite course of Fact Retrieval | £1.15* | Tells you how to revise. Learn how to get shed-loads of facts into your head without heavy machinery. |

| Exam Tips | £1* | Subject specific exam tips. Sugar-coated exam-quenchers. |

just eight & a bit squid

TOTAL = £8.15